Musical Theatre

by Cathy West

Ransom

StarStruck

Musical Theatre
by Cathy West

Illustrated by Martin Bolchover

Published by Ransom Publishing Ltd.
Radley House, 8 St. Cross Road, Winchester, Hants. SO23 9HX
www.ransom.co.uk

ISBN   978 184167 483 4
First published in 2011

Musical Theatre

Contents

All About Musical Theatre

“ When the emotion is too strong to speak, you sing.

When it is too strong for song, you dance. ”

What is musical theatre?

Musical theatre mixes music, songs, spoken words and dance.

Together, they always tell a story.

Many musicals are based on famous stories.

West Side Story is based on the story of Romeo and Juliet. The Phantom of the Opera is from a famous book.

The three main parts of a musical are:

✱ the **music**

✱ the **lyrics** (the words to the music) and

✱ the **book**. The book means the story and the spoken words.

Together, the music and the lyrics are called the **score**.

You can see musical theatre **live** on stage. Or you can see it in a **movie**.

The big shows are in the **West End** in London, or **Broadway** in New York.

But you can put on musical theatre shows anywhere:

 In your local **theatre**.

 Or in your local **school** or **drama club**.

Timeline – musical theatre

When?	Who? Where?	What?
5th Century BCE	The Ancient Greeks	They included music and dance in their plays.
3rd Century BCE	The Romans	Attached metal chips to their shoes – called sabilla – to make the dancing louder. The first tap shoes.
2nd Century BCE	India	Sanskrit drama combining music and dance.
16th Century CE	Italy	Theatre with masked actors, music and dance. Called commedia dell'arte (Italian for 'comedy of art').
1866	New York	The Black Crook. The first musical theatre? It ran for five and a half hours.
1927	New York	The roaring twenties. Show Boat – the first true musical play?

The Black Crook

When?	Who? Where?	What?
1935	USA	Porgy and Bess.
1940s – 1960s	USA	The Golden Age of musical theatre.
1943	USA	Oklahoma! – it ran for 2,212 performances.
1950	USA	Guys and Dolls. Made into a film – with Marlon Brando and Frank Sinatra.
1970s	Rock musicals	Jesus Christ Superstar, Godspell.
1980s	Big budget musicals	Les Misérables, Miss Saigon, The Phantom of the Opera, Evita, Cats.
1990s – 2000s	Movie musicals	Evita, Moulin Rouge!, Mamma Mia!, The Cat in the Hat.

Famous shows

Show Boat

The first performance of Show Boat was in 1927 in New York, USA.

It was written by Jerome Kern and Oscar Hammerstein II.

People called it 'the first true American musical play.'

Oklahoma!

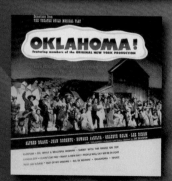

Written by Richard Rodgers and Oscar Hammerstein II.

It was a box office smash!

Oklahoma! opened on Broadway in 1943 and ran for 2,212 performances.

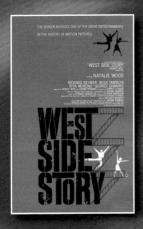

The third great American musical. Leonard Bernstein wrote the music. Stephen Sondheim wrote the lyrics.

The story is about two street gangs, the Jets and the Sharks, in 1950s America.

A film version was made in 1961. The film won ten Academy Awards.

The Phantom of the Opera

The music was written by Andrew Lloyd Webber. He also wrote the music for Jesus Christ Superstar, Joseph and the Amazing Technicolor Dreamcoat, Evita and Cats.

The Phantom of the Opera opened in the West End in London in 1986.

The show has now been seen in 149 cities in 25 countries. It has played to over 100 million people.

Andrew Lloyd Webber

11

Musical theatre around the world

Musicals are performed all around the world.

They are most popular in the UK and the USA. But you can see musicals in many other countries.

Bollywood

India makes many musical films each year. They are called 'Bollywood' musicals (from Bombay and Hollywood).

Bollywood films are often romantic musicals. They are now very popular around the world.

Did you know?

Many Bollywood movies are now filmed in Switzerland!

Japanese musical theatre

Japanese Noh theatre is a very old style of dance theatre.

It started in the fourteenth century.

The actors wear masks. Men play both the male and female parts.

In Japan there is a new kind of musical theatre. It has animations and live action. It is based on anime and manga.

Two popular shows are:

Kiki's Delivery Service. A fantasy musical movie.

The Prince of Tennis Musical. A live musical theatre show, based on a manga series.

13

Jobs in musical theatre

Hundreds of people can work on a big musical theatre show.

Performers

The actors, singers and dancers.

Musicians

Some shows need a very big orchestra.

Composer and lyricist

The composer writes the music. The lyricist writes the words. (One person might do both!)

Director

The person in charge of the whole show. A big job!

Stage Manager (SM)

During a show, the SM is in charge of everything that happens on the stage, as well as backstage.

Other jobs

Choreographer

(Or dance director.) Works out the dance moves.

Set designer

Modern shows have very realistic sets. In Miss Saigon a helicopter lands on the stage during the show. A big headache!

Lighting designer

Decides how to light the show.

Producer

Gets the money to pay for the show. Shows can cost tens of millions of pounds.

Costume designer

Actors need to look good. But they must be able to dance in their costumes too!

A career in musical theatre

Do you want to sing and dance on the stage?

Or do you want a job as a stage manager, or a designer?

How do you start?

Jobs in musical theatre are hard to find.

There are only a few jobs – and lots of people want them!

16

You can go to college to study musical theatre.

This can be a good thing to do.

But get some practice, too.

Maybe you can sing. Maybe you can act. Maybe you can dance.

But can you act and sing and dance – all at the same time?

Tips

⭐ See as many musicals as you can, on stage or screen.

⭐ Study the musicals you like and figure out what makes them good.

⭐ Study the musicals you don't like and figure out why they aren't good!

Dilemma

Chapter One

What to write?

Alice was a writer. She wrote books.

One day a book publisher phoned her. They asked her to write a story about musical theatre.

'Yes, of course,' said Alice. But now she had to think of a story.

Her publisher told her that the Romans put metal bits on their shoes, to make a noise. The Romans invented tap dancing.

But Alice couldn't think of a story about this. Her mind was blank.

The Romans invented the first tap shoes. Why don't you write a story about that?

Hmmm. OK!

But Alice couldn't think of anything to write.

Alice had a daughter, called Kim. Kim liked musical theatre. She was learning about it at school.

Alice had a good idea. She would ask Kim to help her with the story about musical theatre.

'I need some ideas for my story,' Alice said to Kim. 'Have you got any ideas I can use?'

Kim thought about it. 'Yes,' she said at last.

Chapter Two

The first idea

'A girl is watching dancing on TV. She is watching the Cheeky Charlie show. On the show there's a guy she likes,' Kim said.

'That sounds great. Let me write it down.' Alice grabbed her pen and her notebook.

'So the girl wants to be on the Cheeky Charlie show too. She wants to dance on the show,' said Kim. 'But her Mum tells her she can't go on the show because she is a bit too … plump.'

Alice sighed. She put her pen down.

'This can't be my story,' Alice said. 'This is the story for **Hairspray**. That's a famous musical.'

Alice crossed out the notes she had written.

'Do you have any other ideas for a story about musical theatre?' she asked.

Kim thought about it. 'Yes,' she said. 'I have a great idea.'

Chapter Three

The second idea

'This girl and this boy meet on holiday,' said Kim.

'This sounds good – a holiday romance!' said Alice. She grabbed her pen and started to write in her notebook again.

'After the holiday they have to leave each other,' said Kim. 'They both go back to school. But the girl's dad changes his job. And the girl ends up at the same school as the boy she met on holiday.'

Alice put her pen down.

Kim had her second idea ...

'Let me guess,' said Alice. 'The boy and his friends build a car. And they sing a song called **Grease Lightning**.'

'Yes, that's right! How did you know?' Kim said.

Alice laughed. 'That's the plot for **Grease**. We can't use that.'

'Do you have any other ideas?' asked Alice.

Kim thought about it. 'Yes,' she said.

Do they sing a song called **Grease Lightning**?
How did you guess?
That's the story for **Grease**. I can't write that.
Anything else?

Chapter Four

No idea!

'There's a boy who wants to be a ballet dancer. But his dad won't let him,' Kim said.

'No! That's **Billy Elliot**!' Alice laughed. 'Next!'

'There's this pride of lions ...' Kim began.

'Do you have any ideas that haven't been done before?' Alice asked.

Kim thought about it. She laughed. 'No! I don't,' she said.

Alice groaned. 'Then I will have to think of a story on my own.'

Kim had some more ideas ...
You're not doing ballet!
The Circle of Life
No! No! ...

Alice looked at her notebook. Her mind was blank. What could she write about musical theatre?

Then she had an idea. She picked up her pen and wrote in her notebook:

Alice was a writer. She wrote books.

One day a book publisher asked her to write a story about musical theatre. Now Alice had to think of a story.

Alice had a daughter called Kim. Kim liked musical theatre.

Alice had a good idea. She would ask Kim to help her with the story about musical theatre.

Now Alice had her story!

34

Curtain Call

Andrew Lloyd Webber

anime

Bollywood

choreographer

composer

costume designer

director

emotion

Guys and Dolls

Jerome Kern

Leonard Bernstein

lighting designer

lyricist

manga

musician

Noh theatre

Oklahoma!

Oscar Hammerstein II

performer

producer

Richard Rogers

Sanskrit drama

set designer

Show Boat

stage manager

Stephen Sondheim

The Phantom of the Opera

West Side Story